"Hello! I'm

Mr Happy

. Just look at my happy smile, always smiling back at me from every

mirror ."

"Except last Tuesday. I went into the  and looked in the mirror. But my  had gone!"

bathroom

smile

"I didn't know where it had gone. I looked for it in the , and there I saw , laughing."

woods

Mr Funny

"Look at all the smiling  rabbits and  flowers ," he said. "Well, they might have been, but I wasn't."

"My lovely didn't want to come back. Suddenly, a big puff of bright appeared."

smile

red smoke

"And an old  stepped out."

wizard

"Why do you look so unhappy,

?" asked the wizard.

Mr Happy

"Open your wide," he
mouth

said. "I can see your very best

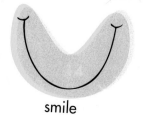 , stuck in your throat."
smile

"The  vanished, this time

wizard

in a great big puff of  .

blue smoke

How could I unstick my smile?"

"First, I tried jumping from a tall tree. No smile. Then I rolled down a big hill Still no smile."

"I went home and sat in front of a
mirror
. And waited. It grew

dark and the 🌙 moon came up."

"It had a big wrinkly  on its

grin

face. I fell fast asleep in a

chair

,

and dreamt about my best smile."

"Next day, I still didn't have my smile back. I went into my  .

garden

All the  had huge smiles."

birds

"Even the frogs in my  puod

seemed happier than ever. I'd say it

was the happiest garden I knew."

"But then a big red made a loud 'POP!' right behind me.

balloon

Little Miss Naughty

had popped it."

"What a shock!" I said. "I almost

jumped as high as my  !"

frogs

But  giggled and said:

Little Miss Naughty

"Look! I've unstuck your smile!" "So I looked in a  . And sure

mirror

enough, there was a smile. In fact, it was my very best  ever!"

smile